A PALACE FOR WEDNESDAY

A PALACE FOR WEDNESDAY

Created by
ALICE HUDSON

Text by
JOHN DARCY NOBLE

Based on Conversations with
ALICE HUDSON

MINGEI INTERNATIONAL MUSEUM

A PALACE FOR WEDNESDAY

Photography   Lynton Gardiner
                    Anthony Scoggins   pages 83, 103, 107

THIS BOOK IS MADE POSSIBLE BY THE SEYMOUR E. CLONICK AND SYDNEY MARTIN ROTH PUBLICATION FUND.

ISBN 0-914155-16-4

Library of Congress Control Number: 2002115221

Published by

MINGEI INTERNATIONAL MUSEUM

1439 El Prado San Diego CA 92101

155 West Grand Avenue Escondido CA 92025

www.mingei.org   www.see-mingei.org

or more than a decade at Mingei International Museum A PALACE FOR WEDNESDAY has been a beloved treasure for children and adults first to discover and, then, to return to visit. It came to us, first on loan and, later, as a museum purchase from the collection of John Darcy Noble. Living in retirement in San Diego County in the 1980s and '90s, John Darcy Noble served on this Museum's International Advisory Board and curated two exhibitions: FIRST COLLECTIONS – Dolls and Folk Toys of the World, 1987 – 88, and DOLLS – Mirrors of Humanity, 1997 – 99. He was a dear friend and colleague of many staff members and a constant source of delight and whimsy. One of the first museum curators of toys in the United States of America, John was also an enchanting artist, writer of published books on dolls, unpublished, magical stories, and a raconteur of great wit. John died at 83 years of age in September 2003.

Mingei International Museum staff members have become acquainted with Alice Hudson through John and by telephone and letter. We all wish we could know her face to face – as will everyone who picks up this book. She has created a magical world to astonish and delight. It is a great pleasure to make Wednesday, her palace and its charmed and charming residents available, at last, to a wider public.

Two special features of this book are accompanying translations of the English text in Spanish and Japanese and a delightful introductory tour on DVD of A PALACE FOR WEDNESDAY conducted by John Darcy Noble and recorded in 1999.

PALACE FOR WEDNESDAY *began when my friend Alice Hudson made me a birthday present. Alice is a very gentle, private person, and in her late 50s she ran away from her everyday life to live very quietly in the deep country.*

Every day she walks in the woods or rambles along the seashore, gathering up shells and feathers and leaves. She has invented a world of faeries which is more real to her than the world outside.

My present was a charming little elfin creature. She was called WEDNESDAY *because my birthday fell on a Wednesday. She is the most delicious, raggedy faerie. My birthday is the first day of spring so, of course,* WEDNESDAY *is most spring-like, with wild silken hair, literally dancing for joy.*

Now, I was on my way to England and couldn't leave this enchanting little creature behind, so what did I do? I put WEDNESDAY *in the breast pocket of my coat, from which she watched the clouds through the airplane window. When I got to the house in England, there were flowers in my bedroom, and I thought this was a perfect place for* WEDNESDAY *to stay. I had forgotten that in England flowers are so important that they are replaced every day.* WEDNESDAY *was rescued from the dustbin, thank goodness! On returning to America, I said, "Alice, this will not do. You must make* WEDNESDAY *a little house so that she will be safe." And Alice said, "But I can't make architecture until May because I'm too near the ocean, and the glue won't dry."*

continued page 12

A PALACE FOR WEDNESDAY
front view, 55" x 45" x 36"

left side view

right side view

So she began in May. Soon I began getting telephone reports. "There's a big kitchen, with a stove made from a goose's egg. There's a theatre." When I asked, "Why a theatre?" Alice replied, "Well, I've made a rock group." "A rock group?" "They're sitting on rocks," she replied.

"There's a beautiful bedroom for WEDNESDAY, with a bedcover made of rose petals. And there's a clock tower; a young poet has retreated to it, and when WEDNESDAY wants to know the time, he blows her a dandelion clock. I added a marvelous room with movable walls. Only WEDNESDAY didn't like it, so it's gone."

When the Palace was finally ready for viewing in August 1981, it was five feet high. And Alice said, "I'm afraid there are rather a lot of people because they keep showing up, WEDNESDAY's friends and relations; and I really can't turn anyone away." You see, these are all very real people to Alice, and she is very concerned about their welfare. In the end there are more than sixty faerie people and two dragons now living in the Palace!

A PALACE FOR WEDNESDAY *was first exhibited for many years at the Museum of the City of New York, where I was Curator of the Toy Collection. In November 1999 it became a part of the permanent collection of Mingei International Museum in Balboa Park, San Diego, California, where it continues to delight children and adults from all around the world.*

Alice and I are very happy that this should be so.

December 1999

A PALACE FOR WEDNESDAY

ウェンズディは、戸口に立って踊る可憐な妖精です。 その下にあるのはジェイスンの梯子、ウェンズディが翼を持ってないため下りて来ることができない, そこで梯子をつくった5歳児にちなんで命名されたのです。

WEDNESDAY is the tiny elf dancing on the doorstep.

Below her is JASON'S LADDER, named for the 5-year-old who made the ladder because WEDNESDAY has no wings and couldn't get down.

MIÉRCOLES es la pequeña elfa que danza en el umbral de la puerta. Abajo está LA ESCALERA DE JASÓN, llamada así por el niño de cinco años que la hizo, porque MIÉRCOLES no tiene alas y no podía bajar.

遍歴の騎士と，その雄々しい駿馬ポピーヘッドは，間もなく到着です。

THE KNIGHT ERRANT
and his brave steed, POPPYHEAD,
soon will be arriving.

EL CABALLERO ERRANTE y su valiente corcel, CABEZA DE AMAPOLA, pronto llegarán.

アングロサクソンのメッセンジャー

THE ANGLO-SAXON MESSENGER

EL MENSAJERO ANGLOSAJÓN

小さいこの人は，ウェンズディと一言交わすのを待っています。

This LITTLE PERSON
is waiting for a word
with WEDNESDAY.

Esta PEQUEÑA PERSONA está esperando para cruzar unas palabras con MIÉRCOLES.

ゴシップする人たち。去年の夏以来、彼らは喋りっぱなしです。

THE GOSSIPS

They have been chattering away since last summer.

LAS HABLANTINAS | Han estado comadreando desde el verano pasado.

夏のゴースト（幽霊）。ゴーストは，色褪せた葉や枯れた花がある限り、ウロウロとあたりを彷徨っているのです。

THE GHOST OF SUMMER

She lingers as long as there is a faded leaf
or a dried flower.

LA ESPÍRITU DEL VERANO | Ella permanece mientras haya una hoja de color esfumado o una flor seca.

彼女の右側には「森の中の全く世間知らず」と彫り込まれた柱が立っています。

On her right is the column where
THE BABES IN THE WOOD
are sculpted.

A su derecha está la columna donde se esculpen LOS NIÑOS DE LOS BOSQUES.

秋の庭から、孤独の人とその娘たちが姿を現します。母親は家族に向かって歌います「みんなに喜んでもらえるように　ブローチや玩具をつくりましょう。」　うしろにあるのはレバス（判じ絵）の門です。

THE LONELY ONE and her daughters emerge from the AUTUMN GARDEN. The mother sings to her family, "I will make you brooches and toys for your delight...."

Behind them is THE REBUS GATE.

LA SOLA y sus hijas emergen del JARDÍN DEL OTOÑO. La madre canta a su familia: "Les haré broches y juguetes para su deleite…" Tras ellas, está LA PUERTA DE LOS JEROGLÍFICOS.

お城の道化者。その役割は、ウェンズディを笑わせる事、極めて楽なお仕事です。

THE PALACE JESTER

His job is to make WEDNESDAY laugh.
It's a very easy job.

EL BUFÓN DEL PALACIO | Su trabajo es hacer reír a MIÉRCOLES. Es un trabajo muy fácil.

緑色の裸の魔女は，ウェンズディのぼんやり税理士、衣服を忘れ、呪文も、会計事務所への道すら、忘れてしまったのです。

THE NAKED GREEN WITCH
is WEDNESDAY's absent-minded accountant.
She forgot her clothes, her spells and the way
to the counting house.

LA BRUJA DESNUDA Y VERDE es la contadora olvidadiza de MIÉRCOLES. Se le olvidaron su ropaje, sus conjuros y el camino a la casa contable.

百花香。このふくよかな小さい人は、バラの花片を縫い込んだドレスに身をつつみ、夏の庭に座っています。

POTPOURRI

This plump little person has rose petals sewn into her dress.
She sits in the SUMMER GARDEN.

POPURRÍ | Esta regordeta y pequeña persona tiene pétalos de rosa cosidos a su vestido.
Se sienta en EL JARDÍN DEL VERANO.

「私はここよ　小さな　ジャンピング　ジョーン　側には誰もいやしない　いつも　一人ぼっちの私です。」

"Here I am, little JUMPING JOAN,
When nobody's with me
I'm always alone."

"JUANITA BRINCONA | ésta soy yo. | Cuando estoy sola, | sola estoy yo".

ミュージシャンたちは劇場で演奏、ウェンズディのロック・グループのメンバーです。

MUSICIANS,
members of WEDNESDAY's rock group, perform in the Theatre.

LOS MÚSICOS, integrantes de la banda roquera de MIÉRCOLES, se presentan en el teatro.

王女様。王女はじっと座って、刺繍のサンプルを刺しているはずなのに、どうして翼を持つ人だけが留り座れる高台に達し得たのかは不明です。

THE INFANTA

She is supposed to sit still and stitch her sampler.
We don't know how she got up to this perch
which was meant for a person with wings.

LA INFANTA | Se supone que debe sentarse quieta y bordar su muestrario. No sabemos cómo se subió a esta percha que se suponía era para una persona alada.

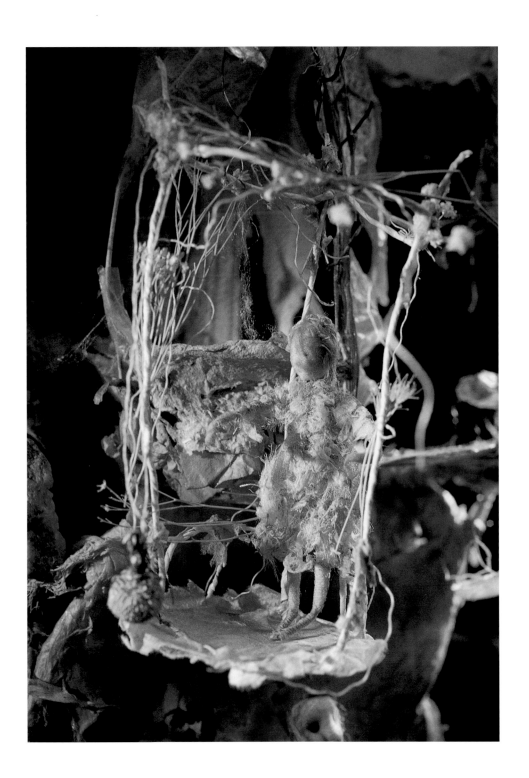

お城の開城が布告された時，滞在するためにやってきた遠い親類

A DISTANT RELATIVE
who came to stay when the Palace was declared open

UN PARIENTE LEJANO que vino a quedarse cuando se declaró abierto el palacio

空中でバランスをとっているのは、ボールを手玉にとる曲芸師ジャグラーとその家族です。
彼は、手際鮮やかで大胆不敵、みんなはそのやり方に倣うのです。

Balanced in midair are the JUGGLER and FAMILY.
He is clever and daring. His family takes after him.

Suspendidos están el JUGLAR y FAMILIA. Él es listo y osado. Su familia es como él.

ウェンズディの寝室には壁がありません。彼女は、4本の柱に支えられた、バラの花びらの散る、クイーン・アンのレースの上掛けが掛かっている寝台に眠ります。そうして鏡は、葡萄の蔦が描かれた台の上に据えられているのです。

WEDNESDAY'S BEDROOM has no walls.
She sleeps in a four-poster bed made of Queen Anne's Lace,
with a rose-petal coverlet. Her mirror rests upon
a grapevine stand.

LA RECÁMARA DE MIÉRCOLES no tiene paredes. Duerme en una cama de cuatro postes hechos de zanahorias silvestres y con un cobertor de pétalos de rosa. Una vid sostiene su espejo.

ひそひそ話しと囁き声、それは住んでいる詩人たちが、話し込んでいるのです。と，我々は思うのですが，誰一人としてその会話をきくことは出来ません。

WHISPER AND MURMUR
are the resident poets in deep conversation. We assume they're speaking to each other, but no one else can hear them.

SUSURRO Y MURMULLO son los poetas del palacio sumergidos en una profunda conversación. Suponemos que están platicando, puesto que nadie puede escucharlos.

王女様アン、バラ色のリンゴのはいったバスケットを抱えて、苺品評会からご帰還

PRINCESS ANNE,
returning from Strawberry Faire
with a basket of rosy apples

LA PRINCESA ANA, regresando de la Feria de las Fresas con una canasta de manzanas rosadas

「バラの花びら」母親ドラゴンは、台所の裏にある洞に住んでいて、その火のような息で、お城を温かく保ちます。彼女の赤ちゃん「バラの蕾み」は、目を閉じたまま体はまだ半分卵の殻の中です。ウェンズディは、「バラの花びら」が、自分の吐く息の強さを知らないせいで、「バラの蕾」を傷つけてはならないと、小さい妖精を雇って団扇で扇ぎます。妖精は、真剣にその任務にあたるのです。

ROSEPETAL,
the mother dragon, lives in a cave behind the kitchen
and keeps the Palace warm with her fiery breath.
Her baby, ROSEBUD, is still half out of her shell;
her eyes are closed. THE LITTLEST ELF is hired by
WEDNESDAY to fan the baby because ROSEPETAL doesn't
know the strength of her heat. He takes his job very seriously.

PÉTALO DE ROSA, la mamá dragona, vive en una cueva tras la cocina y mantiene tibio el palacio con su ardiente aliento. Su bebé, BOTÓN DE ROSA, está a medio salir de su cascarón; sus ojos están cerrados. EL MÁS PEQUEÑO DE LOS ELFOS fue contratado por MIÉRCOLES para abanicar a la bebé, porque PÉTALO DE ROSA no sabe de la intensidad de su calor. Él toma su trabajo con mucha seriedad.

ヴァイオレットは真新しい乳母車で初めて外出です。私はアリスに云いました，「だけど，お母さんは何処なの？」 彼女答えて曰く，「あのね、私知らないの、ヴァィオレットも知らないわ。」

VIOLET
is out for the first time in her new baby carriage.
I said to Alice, "But where is her mother?" And she said,
"Well, I don't know, and neither does VIOLET."

VIOLETA sale por primera vez en su nueva carriola. Le pregunté a Alicia: "¿Dónde está su mamá?" Y ella respondió: "No lo sé y tampoco VIOLETA lo sabe".

無邪気なサイモンは、お城での夕食のためパイを買っています。ここでもう一つの童謡です「無邪気なサイモン　品評会に向かう　パイつ"くりのおじさんに出会いました。サイモンがいうには　どうでしょう　その品をお味見させて下さいませんか。」

SIMPLE SIMON
is buying pies for the Palace dinner.

Here is another nursery rhyme:
"Simple Simon met a pieman going to the fair.
Said Simon to the pieman,
'let me taste your wares.'"

SIMÓN EL BOBITO está comprando pasteles para la cena en el palacio.
Aquí está otra rima infantil: "Simón el bobito llamó al pastelero: | "¡a ver los pasteles, | los quiero probar!"

壁にかかっている神秘的なお面の後ろにあるのは、ジェイスンの秘密の食器棚、そこには
ジェイスンが、ウェンズディに、来年の夏まで預かってくれるようにと託した、白い蛾が残さ
れていました。

Behind the MYSTERIOUS FACE in the wall
is JASON'S SECRET CUPBOARD, where Jason
left a white moth for WEDNESDAY to mind
until summer comes again.

Tras LA MISTERIOSA CARA en la pared se encuentra el ARMARIO SECRETO DE JASÓN, donde él dejó
una polilla blanca para que MIÉRCOLES la cuidara hasta que regresara el verano.

男の子は、お城の階段を登り下りして生活に必要な品々を運びます。

A BOY carries provisions
up the Palace staircase.

UN NIÑO sube provisiones por la escalera del palacio.

不思議な力のある手を持つ魔法使い

THE WIZARD WITH THE MAGIC HANDS

EL MAGO DE LAS MANOS MÁGICAS

デンデン虫の操り手とデンデン虫たち。色とりどりの年とったデンデン虫は，ウェンズディが それは大切にしているペットです。何かあっては大変と，その世話のため世話人をやとって餌 を与え、見守っています。

SNAILKEEPER and SNAILS

These colorful old snails are WEDNESDAY's favorite pets. She hired a keeper to look after and feed them because she was afraid they would get lost.

EL CARACOLERO Y CARACOLES | Estos coloridos y viejos caracoles son las mascotas preferidas de MIÉRCOLES. Contrató un caracolero para que los alimentara y cuidara pues temía que se perdieran.

小さな妖精

A LITTLE FAERIE

UNA PEQUEŃA HADA

ベイビー・ラパンゼルを盗もうとしている魔女は、お城の壁に掛かっている彫刻です。

THE WITCH STEALING BABY RAPUNZEL
is a sculpture on the Palace wall.

LA BRUJA ROBANDO A LA BEBÉ RAPUNZEL es una escultura en el muro del palacio.

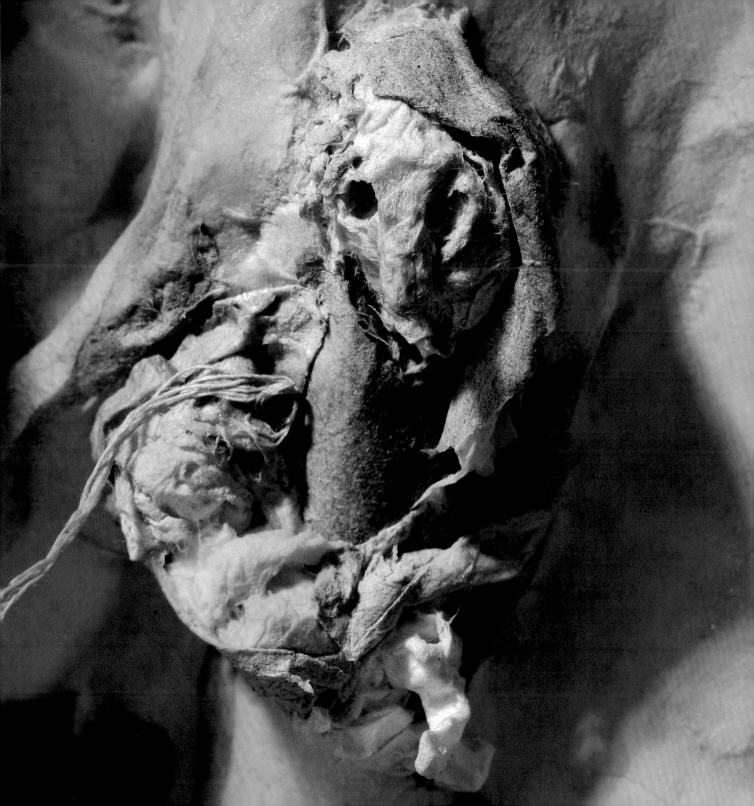

怒っている鬼。彼は、その森を荒らし、せせらぎを汚す、無頓着な人々にカンカンです。

THE ANGRY GOBLIN

He is furious with the careless people who litter his woods
and pollute his streams.

EL GNOMO ENOJADO | Está furioso con la gente descuidada que tira basura en sus bosques
y contamina sus arroyos.

浮彫りは、白鳥の王子さま。マジック・コートの完成が間に合わず、そのためいつも、片側の白鳥の羽が覗いて見えるのです。

In sculptural relief is THE SWAN PRINCE.
His magic coat was not finished in time;
thus he always kept one swan wing.

En un relieve escultórico está EL PRÍNCIPE CISNE. Su gabán mágico no fue terminado a tiempo, por eso siempre conservó un ala de cisne.

時計台。そこは実をいうと、一人でいたいもう一人の詩人の家なのです。一人とはいえ、彼はタンポポでつくられた時計のコレクションを持っています。ウェンズディは、何時なのか知りたい時、彼に向かって呼びかけます、彼はそれに答えて時計を鳴らす、その結果、何を書こうとしていたのかを忘れるのです。

THE CLOCK TOWER

It's actually a home for another poet, who wants to be solitary;
but he has a collection of dandelion clocks. When WEDNESDAY wants
to know the time, she calls up to him; and he blows the clock
for her — and forgets what he was going to write.

LA TORRE DEL RELOJ | De hecho, es el hogar de otro poeta que quiere estar solo, pero tiene una colección de relojes de diente de león. Cuando MIÉRCOLES quiere saber la hora le llama, él sopla el diente de león... y se le olvida lo que iba a escribir.

ほぼ死滅（絶滅近し）。この動物は、年老いて動けません。それに、食べ物である月桂樹の実（一日一個）は，最早手の届く岩壁の棚には生えていないのです。親切な妖精は、同じように高齢で，寝室用のスリッパで這い登るのが困難になっているのですが、彼を愛しているので，毎日食事をさせるためにやって来るのです。

ALMOST EXTINCT

This animal is too old to move, and the bayberries that he eats (one a day) no longer grow on his ledge. A kind faerie comes every day to feed him, although she is old too, and it's a hard climb in bedroom slippers. But, then, she loves him.

CASI EXTINTO | Este animal es demasiado viejo para moverse y las bayas de myrica que come (una diaria) ya no crecen en su cornisa. Un hada amable viene todos los días a alimentarlo aunque ella también es vieja y es difícil escalar con pantuflos… pero, bueno, es que lo ama.

ケアフリー。ウェンズディの親友の一人であるケアフリーは、我々を歓迎して歌います。「私は何も気にしない　風にのって踊る時　心は燕の翼の羽そのままに　身軽なもの。名前すら忘れて　気ままなお天気に身を托し　喜び一杯踊ります。」

CAREFREE,
one of WEDNESDAY's close friends, singing a song to welcome us:

"I care for nothing
As I dance on the wind
And my heart is as light
As a lark's wing feather.
And I can't even bother
To remember my name
As I dance with delight
In the whirlaway weather."

DESPREOCUPADA, una de las amigas más cercanas de MIÉRCOLES, canta una canción para darnos la bienvenida: "Por nada me preocupo ni altero | cuando bailo en el viento. | Mi corazón es ligero, | como pluma de alondra lo siento. | Ni me puedo molestar | en mi nombre recordar | al bailar con deleite que admira | en el tiempo que gira y gira".

緑の子供たち、ウェンズディのお城への道を発見

THE GREEN CHILDREN,
who found their way to WEDNESDAY's Palace

LOS NIÑOS VERDES, que encontraron cómo llegar al palacio de MIÉRCOLES

塔の高い部分は光の標識，それは，着陸のため流れ糸のプラットフォームに接近するとき、翼をもつ訪問者たちが皆一様に，遠くからでも見ることが出来るのです。

High in the tower is a BEACON OF LIGHT,
which can be seen from far away by all the winged visitors as they make
their approach to the gossamer LANDING PLATFORM.

En lo alto de la torre está un HAZ DE LUZ que puede ser visto desde muy lejos por todos los visitantes alados cuando se aproximan a la delicada y afiligranada PLATAFORMA DE ATERRIZAJE.

逃げ出した王女様。両親は、退屈な王子様と結婚させたい、そうしてお城に住んでそこで髪を梳くようにと願っているのですが, 彼女は風と一緒になりたいのです。

THE RUNAWAY PRINCESS

Her parents want her to marry some tiresome prince
and live in a castle and comb her hair,
but she wants to marry the wind.

LA PRINCESA FUGITIVA | Sus padres quieren que se case con algún príncipe pesado, viva en un castillo y cepille su cabello, pero ella quiere casarse con el viento.

この訪問者は、彼の小さい伯父さんと共に到着しました。二人はどこに行くのも一緒です。

THE VISITOR,
who arrived with his small uncle

These two go everywhere together.

EL VISITANTE que llegó con su pequeño tío. | Ellos dos van juntos a todas partes.

ドイツ，ババリア地方の王女さま。この小さい人はでしゃばりです。一体，彼女が何処から
やって来たのか，アリスは確かではありません，ババリアの王女だとの自称ですが。
ウェンズディは，それは親切なので滞在するのを許しているのです。でも、彼女ときたら
ありとあらゆる事に批判的で、傲慢にも，全て自分の生れた国のほうがうんと良いと信じて
いるのです。

THE BAVARIAN PRINCESS

This little person is an interloper.
Alice wasn't sure where she came from. She says she's a Bavarian princess.
And WEDNESDAY is so kind, she let her stay. But she criticizes
everything and arrogantly believes it's all much better in her homeland.

LA PRINCESA BÁVARA | Esta pequeña persona es una intrusa; Alicia no estaba segura de dónde vino.
Ella dice que es una princesa bávara y MIÉRCOLES es tan amable que la deja quedarse. Pero ella critica todo y
arrogantemente cree que todo es mucho mejor en su patria.

お馬鹿さん，そのアオカケスの羽で大喜び

THE SIMPLETON,
whose blue jay feather delights him

EL CÁNDIDO, cuya pluma de arrendajo azul lo fascina

舞踏室で, ウェエンズディの祖父は, 孫、ウェンズディの従弟であるチューズデイに、昔々の
お話しをしています。

In the BALLROOM, WEDNESDAY'S GRANDFATHER
tells tales of long ago to his grandson,
WEDNESDAY's cousin, TUESDAY.

En el SALÓN DE BAILE, el ABUELO DE MIÉRCOLES
cuenta historias de antaño a su nieto MARTES, el primo de MIÉRCOLES.

詩人テニスンのマリアナ。「たった一言　彼女がいったのは　一日は荒涼として物哀しく 彼はやって来なかった。」

The poet Tennyson's MARIANA

"she only said, 'the day is dreary. He cometh not,' she said."

MARIANA del poeta Tennyson | "Ella sólo dijo, 'el día es triste. | Él no viene', dijo ella".

ウェンズディのかぶと虫の友人の一人

One of WEDNESDAY's BEETLE FRIENDS

Uno de los AMIGOS ESCARABAJOS de MIÉRCOLES

「緑をまとったヘクター・プロテクター　ヘクター・プロテクター　クイーンの許に送られる。女王は彼を嫌い　王様もまた同じ事。そこでヘクター・プロテクター　再送返。」

"HECTOR PROTECTOR dressed in green,
Hector Protector was sent to the Queen;
The Queen didn't like him,
No more did the King;
So Hector Protector was sent back again."

"Todo de verde HÉCTOR EL PROTECTOR, |
a la reina fue enviado mas no le aprobó; | el rey mucho menos, | así lo indicó, | de modo que Héctor se devolvió".

「雲一杯の霧のこもった濡れた朝　私は皮に身を固めたお年寄りに　たまたま行き合ったのです。」

"One misty, moisty morning, when cloudy was the weather,
I chanced to meet
AN OLD MAN DRESSED ALL IN LEATHER."

"Una mañana tras de un aguacero | cuando el tiempo estaba nublado, |
conocí, pues pasó por mi lado, | a UN ANCIANO VESTIDO DE CUERO".

料理人たちとお皿洗いの人々は，卵の殻でつくられたストーヴが，赤々と熱を放っている大キチンに集合です。

COOKS and SCULLIONS
gather in THE GREAT KITCHEN,
where an eggshell stove glows with heat.

COCINEROS y MARMITONES se reúnen en LA GRAN COCINA
donde una estufa de cascarón de huevo brilla con el calor.

今日のニュースは何でしょう？　ここでもう一つの童謡です。「気のいいお隣りの方
ニュースはナーニ　何でしょう？」　「風船が月にむかって飛び去った　ということだけど。」

WHAT'S THE NEWS OF THE DAY?

Here's another nursery rhyme:
"What's the news, good neighbor, what's the news?"
"I hear a balloon has flown to the moon."

¿CUÁL ES LA NOTICIA DEL DÍA? Aquí está otra rima infantil:
"¿Qué noticia hay, buen vecino, o qué no hay ninguna?" | "Oí que un globo ha volado a la luna".

妖精は騎士がやってくるのを見守る

AN ELF
watching for the knight to come

UN ELFO esperando ver al caballero que vendrá

翼を持つ白い彫刻のドラゴンは，あずまや（見晴し台）の太い横棧にまつわりつく。

THE WINGED WHITE SCULPTURED DRAGON
curls around THE GAZEBO'S LEDGE.

EL BLANCO Y ALADO DRAGÓN ESCULPIDO se enrosca alrededor de LA CORNISA DEL QUIOSCO.

マリゴールド（キンセンカ）の守り神。多くの妖精がそうであるように、この妖精も特別のお花を守っています。彼は何時だって、かぶと虫のお付きに伴われているのです。

THE GUARDIAN OF THE MARIGOLDS

Like many faeries, this one looks after a special flower.
He is always accompanied by his attendant beetle.

EL GUARDIÁN DE LAS MARAVILLAS | Como muchos hados, éste cuida una flor especial.
Siempre está acompañado por su escarabajo ayudante.

ガーゴイル（雨水の落とし口）、お城の壁には蟹の甲羅を頭につけたそれが掛けられています。

THE GARGOYLE
with a crabshell headress
stands sculpted on the Palace wall.

LA GÁRGOLA con su tocado de caparazón de cangrejo se mantiene firme esculpida en el muro del palacio.

ジャック・フロスト（霜）が住んでいる冬の庭園

THE WINTER GARDEN
where JACK FROST lives

EL JARDÍN DE INVIERNO en donde vive EL FRÍO EN PERSONA

家の最上部、一番高いところには、二番目のドラゴンがいて，こちらはより獰猛です。
家を守っていて名前はフレイム（炎）、そのしっぽの妖精は、デリング・ドウーです。

High above, at the top of the house,
is a second dragon; and this is a much fiercer one.
He guards the house, and his name is FLAME.
The elf on his tail is DERRING-DO.

Muy en lo alto, en lo más alto de la casa, está un segundo dragón y es mucho más fiero.
Cuida la casa y se llama FLAMA. El elfo en su cola se llama OSADO.

一体、彼が何人やら、誰も知りません。何処からか, 飛び込んで来たのです。
ウェンズディがそれはやさしく親切なので、滞在を許されたのです。

We don't know who he is.
HE BLEW IN.
And since WEDNESDAY is so friendly,
he was allowed to stay.

No sabemos quién es él. LO TRAJO EL VIENTO.
Y como MIÉRCOLES es tan amistosa, le permitió quedarse.

何処のお城にも、うろうろとさまよい歩く無名の人々がいるのです。

Every palace has people wandering about nameless.

Todos los palacios tienen gente sin nombre que deambula por ellos.

この仲間たちは，人生の旅を継続する前に、一息入れようと足を止めているのです。

These COMPANIONS have stopped to rest
before continuing their journey
on the road of life.

Estos COMPAÑEROS han parado a descansar antes de continuar su travesía por el camino de la vida.

A PALACE FOR WEDNESDAY

by John Darcy Noble

It seems familiar, hauntingly so.
Absurd of course
How could you have seen it before?
It isn't even finished
This Palace for Wednesday.

For days you ponder
While it haunts – beguiles
Until, dreaming at dusk
Among fireflies
You remember.

Your first soap-bubble
In early Springtime
Gleaming, magical
And you longed suddenly
To live in it forever.

Midsummer
And you put away childish things
But clearly, in the sunset clouds
You saw it
A castle, airy and unsubstantial
Banners and pennants shimmering
With rosy light.

In the Autumn
Gazing out to sea
You saw its towers, pinnacles
Wavering, mysterious in the mist.
And you wept with longing.

Even now
As you stir Winter's embers
From the heart of the fire it shines
Magical as ever
The glowing casements wide
The stairs inviting
That you never climbed.

No wonder it's familiar
Unfinished though it is
And of course your heart leaps
At the sight.
This is your birthright, your truest desire.
This is your home at the world's end
Your Palace for Wednesday.

MINGEI
INTERNATIONAL MUSEUM

THE DIRECTOR'S CIRCLE
Members who provide core suppport for the Museum's exhibitions

Kenneth and Dixie Unruh
Co-Chairs

Sumi Adachi and Dan McLeod
Ms. Taryl Andersen
Claire Anderson
Mr. and Mrs. Augusto Angelucci
Mr. Norm Applebaum, AIA and
    Ms. Barbara Roper
Mrs. Frances M. Armstrong
Mr. and Mrs. Bob Baker
Carolyn L. E. Benesh and Robert K. Liu
Dr. and Mrs. H. Kenneth Bishop
Mr. and Mrs. Robert A. Bowden
Tanya and Charles Brandes
Ms. Clara Jo Brown
Ms. Esther J. Burnham
Carmela M. Caldera
Louisa Campagna
Jean Warner Campbell
Mr. and Mrs. Hugh C. Carter
Mr. and Mrs. Jack Charney
Mr. and Mrs. Richard K. Colbourne
Honorable Arthur J. Collingsworth and
    Brian R. Simmons
Dr. Roger C. Cornell
Robert and Elisabeth Crouch
Nancy N. Danninger
Mrs. Alex De Bakcsy
Mr. and Mrs. Eric Denniston
Alice and Doug Diamond
Mr. and Mrs. Charles H. Dick, Jr.
Lois Sherr Dubin
Dr. and Mrs. Renato Dulbecco
Ms. Danah H. Fayman
Carol Fink
Joan Fisher
Leslie and William Foster
Nicholas L. and Leslie Ann Frazee

Mr. Lynton Gardiner
Mr. and Mrs. Arnold Ginnow
Mrs. Connie K. Golden
Lola and Walter Green
Mr. and Mrs. Ernest Hahn, II
Mr. and Mrs. Michael E. Hallor
Jake Harshbarger
Mr. Lars Helgeson
Mr. Richard C. Helmstetter
Mr. and Mrs. Lionel P. Hernholm, Jr.
Mr. William E. Heyler
Ken and Sandy High
Dr. Maryalys K. Hill
Mr. Sam Hilu
Traci Hong
Dr. and Mrs. Author E. Hughes
Carol F. Hinrichs
Alan and Nora Jaffe
Salim Janmohamed
Mr. Gary Jugum
Mr. and Mrs. Neil A. Kjos, Jr.
Mr. and Mrs. Frederick Kleinbub
Dr. and Mrs. Jay Kovtun
Stella Larsen
Mrs. George Lazarnick
Mr. and Mrs. Marvin Levine
Stefanie and Alfred Lord
Mr. and Mrs. William MacKenzie
Peri Marek and Peg Urvoas
M. Lee Maturo
Mr. and Mrs. Edward M. Mayers
Lani and Herb McCoy
Ms. Rena Minisi and Mr. Rich Paul
Capt. and Mrs. Gary Elwyn Monell, USNR(Ret)
Mr. and Mrs. James F. Mulvaney
Henry "Hank" Murphy and Shirley T. Murphy
Mira Nakashima-Yarnall and Kevin Nakashima,
    George Nakashima Woodworker
Ms. Lyn Nelson
Mr. and Mrs. William Norgren

Revs. Carolyn and Tom Owen-Towle
Philip R. and Pamela Palisoul
Tom and Karen Pecht
Mrs. Walter J. Podbielniak
Sheila M. Potiker
Elliott and Diane Rabin
Phil and Pam Reed
Mr. Edward H. Richard and
    Mr. Warren P. Kendrick
Dr. and Mrs. Alan Robbins
Ewa Robinson
Richard and Faye Russell
Mrs. William C. Ruzich
Dr. and Mrs. Joseph D. Schmidt
Curt Sherman
Guy Showley and Jo Bobbie MacConnell
Dr. and. Mrs. Vladimir Shuster
Mr. John R. Siglow
Dr. Robert Singer and Ms. Judith Harris
Mrs. Gwen Stoughton
Ms. Deborah Szekely
Mr. J. L. Tanzer
Mrs. Naomi Thomas
The John M. and
    Sally B. Thornton Foundation
Molly Thornton
Paul Van Elderen
Dr. and Mrs. Andrew Viterbi
Dr. and Mrs. Robert D. Wallace
Dr. and Mrs. Tom A. Waltz
Mr. and Mrs. Howard Weiner
The Weingart-Price Fund
Mr. and Mrs. Jean-René Westfall
Ms. Therese T. Whitcomb
Ann and Phil White
Judy and Jack White
Mr. and Mrs. Harold B. Williams
Mr. and Mrs. Robert K. Wolford
Terri Peterson Zimdars

MINGEI INTERNATIONAL MUSEUM'S acquisition of

A PALACE FOR WEDNESDAY was made possible by a matching grant from

THE HAMILTON-WHITE FOUNDATION and the following generous contributors:

Mr. and Mrs. R. T. Allan
Ms. Nellie Amondson
Ms. Claire Anderson
Mr. Craig S. Andrews
Barbara Baehr
Dr. and Mrs. Charles Ballinger
Mrs. Ina S. Bartell
Ms. Foy Beck and
    Ms. Frances Petefish
Mrs. Clarissa H. Beerbower
Mr. and Mrs. Bill G. Beinert
Mr. and Mrs. Donald Bernstein
Mrs. Eugene Bernstein
Mr. and Mrs. Dumont Blankenship
Ms. Esther J. Burnham
Mrs. Patricia C. Dwinnell Butler
Mrs. Helen Jean Callahan
Ms. Joan S. Campbell
Mr. and Mrs. Martin Carlsen
Mr. and Mrs. Ralph J. Cerbone
Ms. Barbara Chapman
Mr. and Mrs. J. Dallas Clark
Mrs. Barbara Cole
Dr. and Mrs. Joel L. Cook
Mr. and Mrs. George L. Cory
Mrs. Florence Covell
Mr. and Mrs. Lawrence W. Cox
Mrs. Marilynn Crehore
Mrs. Jean Cromwell
Mrs. Elza Cypis

Ms. Linnea B. Dayton
Mr. and Mrs. Wilhelm M. DeHaan
Ms. Pauline Des Granges
Mr. and Mrs. Michael H. Dessent
Mr. and Mrs. Roy Drachman
Mrs. Laura Drucker
Dr. and Mrs. Russell Duff
Dr. Marie-Jo Dulade-Coclet
Mr. and Mrs. Warren Eding
Dr. and Mrs. Charles C. Edwards
Dr. and Mrs. Herbert L. Eisen
Mr. and Mrs. Victor Engleman
Mr. and Mrs. Ronald Erbetta
Mrs. Rebecca Etess
Mrs. Robert Fei
Mr. and Mrs. Herbert Feitler, Jr.
Ms. Lois D. Ferguson
Mr. Walter Fitch, III
Ms. Mary Ellen Fleischli
Ms. Sharon McDade Floyd
Mrs. Isabelle Friedlieb
Dr. Aleene M. Friedman
Mrs. Elena R. Gannon
Mr. and Mrs. Edward Gastelum
Audrey Geisel
Mr. and Mrs. Joe Giammona
Mrs. Arlene Gilbert
Ms. Harriet Gill
Mr. and Mrs. Wally Glozack
Mrs. Milton D. Goldberg

Mrs. Susan Goldberg
Mr. Louis Goldich
Mrs. Norman Gottlieb
Ms. Nathelle Greenleaf
Mr. and Mrs. Denny Gulick
Mrs. Evelyn M. Gulick
Mrs. Judith E. Hannula
Ms. Marilyn B. Harmon
Mr. and Mrs. Robert S. Harper
Ms. Reena Heijdeman
Dr. Dorothy W. Hewes
Mr. William E. Heyler
Mrs. Louise B. Hoffman
Mr. and Mrs. Curtis Holder
Mrs. Jean Hough
Ms. Marjorie Howard-Jones
Ms. Viletta Hutchinson
Mr. Joseph E. Jessop, Jr.
Ms. Sonja F. Jones
Mrs. Louisa S. Kassler
Mr. and Mrs. Bob King
Ms. Leean Knetzer
Mr. August Krause
Mr. and Mrs. Burton Kuck
Mr. and Mrs. Thomas Ladner
Ms. Louise Landau
Ms. Noel S. Leone
Mr. and Mrs. William Mackenzie
Heimple Charitable Foundation
Mrs. Kathryn Madara

Mrs. Frederick T. Marston
Mr. Richard McCartney and
    Ms. Sandra Higgins
Mrs. Christa McReynolds
Mrs. Elaine McVey
Ms. Betsy Meyers
Dr. and Mrs. Victor Moreno
Ms. Patricia Morrison
Ms. Mary Mosson and
    Ms. Donna Cundiff
Ms. Mary E. Murray
Mr. and Mrs. Ralph E. Neiger
Helen M. Nelson
Mrs. John R. Norton, II
Dr. and Mrs. Anton M. Pantone
Mr. and Mrs. Raymond Park
Mrs. Betty-Jo Petersen
Mr. and Mrs. Paul J. Petitmermet
Mr. Henry Petzal
Mr. and Mrs. Lenn Pierson
Ms. Pearl Prine
Ms. Eva Quesenberry
Mrs. Joyce W. Quintana
Mr. and Mrs. Jorgen G. Rasmussen
Dr. and Mrs. Robert W. Rector
Ms. Sheridan Reed
Mrs. James I. Robinson
Niki de Saint Phalle
Mrs. Kathleen A. Scales
Ms. Judy Seerey

Mrs. Marilyn Shaw
Mrs. Wendy Shelton
Mr. and Mrs. Morgan Sinclaire
Ms. Bradley Slayton
Mrs. Tammy Curry Smith
Ms. Suzanne Spector
Mrs. Arlene Stamper
Ms. Dorothy G. Stone
Mr. and Mrs. Robert Strich
Ms. Mary G. Swann
Mr. and Mrs. Theodore T. Tanalski
Mr. and Mrs. Walter Tasem
Mr. and Mrs. Michael Thiemann
Thursday Club
Mr. and Mrs. Richard Waggoner
Mr. and Mrs. Joseph Wagner
Mrs. Thirza B. Wales
Ms. Ricky Warkentin
Mr. and Mrs. Robert Warwick
Mrs. Anita Alvarez Williams
Ms. Shirley Lynn Woolley
Ms. H. A. Terry Yirga
Ms. Sue E. Young

PUBLICATION

Editor	Rob Sidner
Photography	Lynton Gardiner
	Anthony Scoggins pages 83, 103, 107
Book Design	Jonathan Louie Design
Japanese Translation	Sumi Adachi
Spanish Translation	Gabriela Hussong
Jacket Text	Charlotte Cagan
Copyediting / Proofreading	Charlene Baldridge, Martha Ehringer, Lotus Fragola
Fonts	Airstream, Cochin, Adobe Garamond Pro, Hiragino and Kozuka Mincho, Hypatia Sans, Minion Pro, Saphir
Color Separations	Bright Arts, Hong Kong
Paper	Gold East Matte
Printing	Printed in China by Imago

MINGEI INTERNATIONAL MUSEUM, a non-profit, public corporation (IRS section 501(c)(3)), fosters the understanding and appreciation of art of the people (mingei) from all cultures of the world; this art shares a direct simplicity and reflects a joy in making, by hand, useful objects of timeless beauty that are satisfying to the human spirit.

ACCREDITED BY THE AMERICAN ASSOCIATION OF MUSEUMS

The Museum is supported by memberships, volunteer services and tax-deductible donations.

The Museum program is funded in part by the City of San Diego Commission for Arts and Culture and the County of San Diego Community Enhancement Program and Community Projects Fund

ISBN 0-914155-16-4
Library Of Congress Control Number: 2002115221

Published by

MINGEI INTERNATIONAL MUSEUM

1439 El Prado / Balboa Park / San Diego CA 92101 / 619-239-0003
155 West Grand Avenue / Escondido CA 92025 / 760-735-3355
www.mingei.org   www.see-mingei.org